CHARLEY HARPER

Painting complex creatures with simplicity, and without losing their true character, was a signature skill of Charley Harper (American, 1922–2007). He painted animals from all continents, both wild and domestic, and created now famous posters for organizations that care for and protect animals. He combined his talent with a respect for the world's creatures to create artwork that has delighted animal lovers for decades.

Harper grew up on a farm in West Virginia and studied at the Art Students League of New York and the Art Academy of Cincinnati. In 1947 Harper and his wife, Edie, went on a six-month journey through the United States. While at the Grand Canyon, he understood that realism couldn't capture its immensity. Harper decided he must reduce what he saw to its simplest forms—a decision that led directly to his self-described minimal realist style. His classic animal artwork that uses clear geometric forms is perfect for a set of coloring books.

Inside are twenty-two pages of Charley Harper's playful animals, with his full-color illustrations featured on the inside of the front and back covers. Don't forget about the blank pages at the end—we've left them there for you to draw the animals you find in your world.

COLORING BOOK
VOLUME 1

1. The **sea otter** loves to float around and eat, and sometimes it uses tools like rocks to pry open its favorite shellfish. The name of this painting is *Otterly Delicious*.

2. The plump **quail** likes to stay low, foraging and building its nest on the ground.

3. The lucky little **ladybug** is pretty smart, too: its shining red wings and black spots tell predators to stay away. The name of this painting is *Lucky Ladybug*.

4. The brilliant feathers and prideful tail of the **orange-bellied trogon** can be spotted in the humid forest canopies of Panama and Costa Rica.

5. Don't feed the bears! But **black bears** do enjoy munching on berries they find in the wild. The name of this painting is *Blackbeary Jam*.

6. The **hawk** perches up high before diving through the air to catch prey in its sharp talons.

7. The tropical **toucan** uses its huge bill to play a game of fruit toss with its mate.

8. A **calico cat**—with white, orange, and black fur—is almost always a female. The name of this painting is *Limp on a Limb*.

9. Talk about adaptable: the **parrot fish** can change gender and color whenever it wants, and cocoons itself at night to hide from predators.

10. The **puss moth caterpillar** stands tall when a predator approaches.

11. An owl that lives underground may sound odd, but the **burrowing owl** doesn't think so. It nests in holes other animals have left behind.

12. In the Galápagos Islands, the many types of beaks on **Darwin's finches** are so special that they made scientific history. The name of this painting is *Darwin's Finches*.

13. Be mine? The **barn owl** is known for its face shaped like the perfect Valentine's Day heart. The name of this painting is *Vowlentine*.

14. Fishing in groups helps the **pelican** drive prey into shallow water, where it easily scoops up fish in its giant pouch.

15. People may keep the **Gouldian finch** as a pet because of his vibrant feathers, but he lives in the wild in northern Australia.

16. The male **wood duck** is one of the most spectacular creatures on the lake. His glimmering feathers nearly look painted.

17. A **bumblebee** is so hairy that pollen gets caught all over its body. It's smart, and adds this pollen to the day's collection.

18. You may know the **basset hound** as the lovable dog with the long ears, but this pup was made to use its keen sense of smell for hunting.

19. Pairs of **cardinals** communicate through their sweet song phrases. Singing from her nest, the female may be telling her mate when to bring food home. The name of this painting is *Cardinals Consorting*.

20. During autumn migration, the **wood duck** stops in wooded marshes and swamps where there are plenty of acorns and other treats to eat. The name of this painting is *Octoberama*.

21. The **turtle** is one of the oldest types of reptiles, and many are endangered today.

22. Spring and summer flowers attract the tiger-striped **swallowtail butterfly** with their sweet nectar.

 Pomegranate

Pomegranate Communications, Inc.
19018 NE Portal Way, Portland, OR 97230
800-227-1428   pomegranate.com

Color illustrations © 2014 Charley Harper Art Studio
Line drawings © Pomegranate Communications, Inc.

Item No. CB152
ISBN 978-0-7649-6722-1

Designed by Stephanie Odeh and Hisiya Beppu

This product is in compliance with the CPSIA. A General Conformity Certificate and tracking information are available through Pomegranate.

Manufactured and Distributed by Pomegranate Communications, Inc.
Printed in Korea

28 27 26 25 24 23 22 21 20   15 14 13 12 11 10 9 8 7 6

1. The **sea otter** loves to float around and eat, and sometimes it uses tools like rocks to pry open its favorite shellfish.

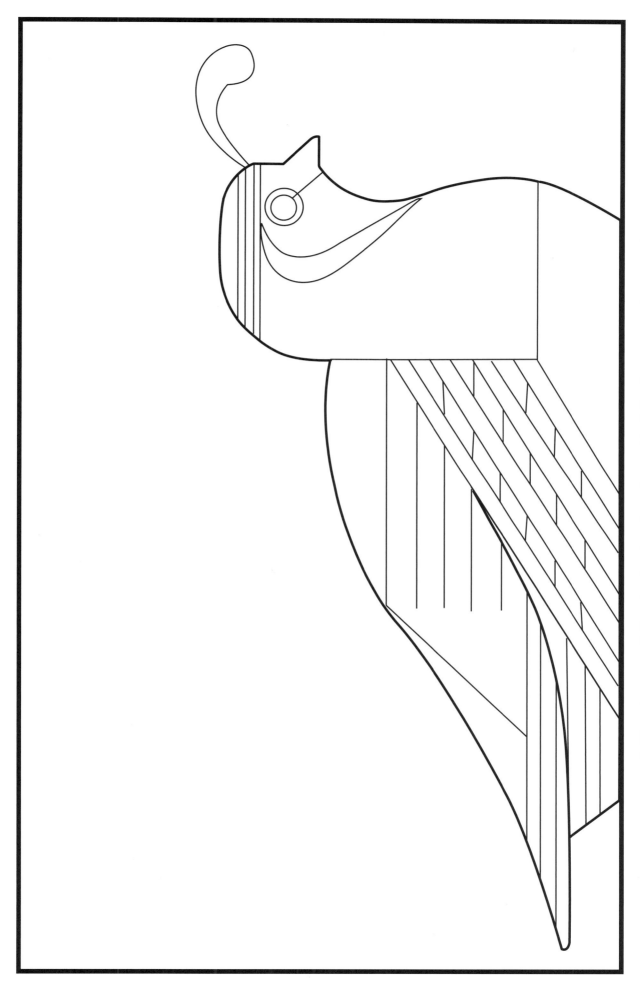

2. The plump **quail** likes to stay low, foraging and building its nest on the ground.

3. The lucky little **ladybug** is pretty smart, too: its shining red wings and black spots tell predators to stay away.

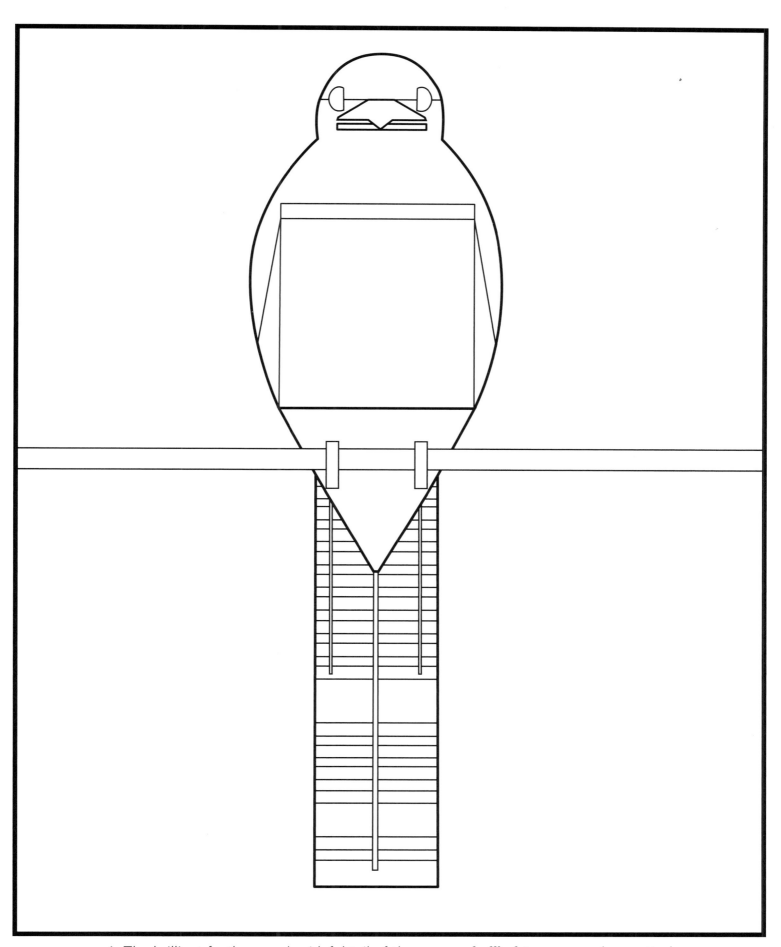

4. The brilliant feathers and prideful tail of the **orange-bellied trogon** can be spotted in the humid forest canopies of Panama and Costa Rica.

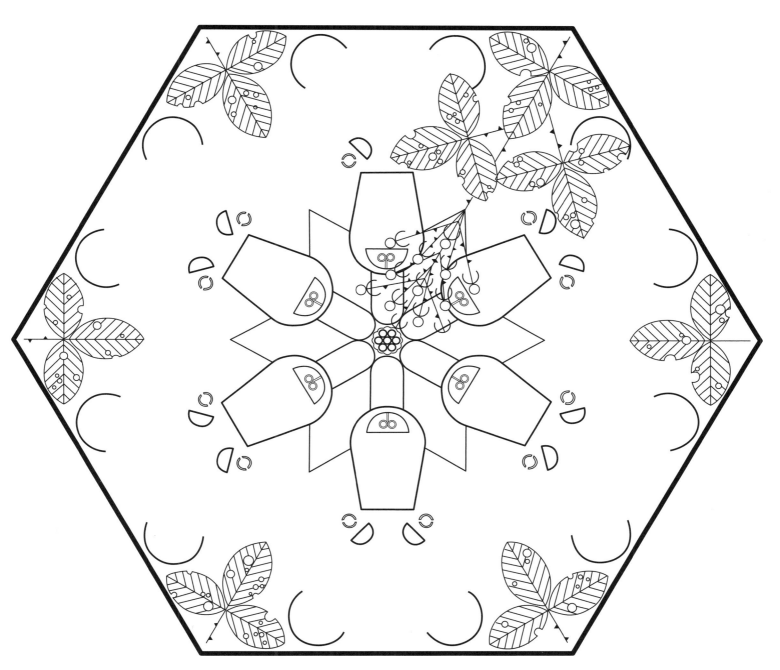

5. Don't feed the bears! But **black bears** do enjoy munching on berries they find in the wild.

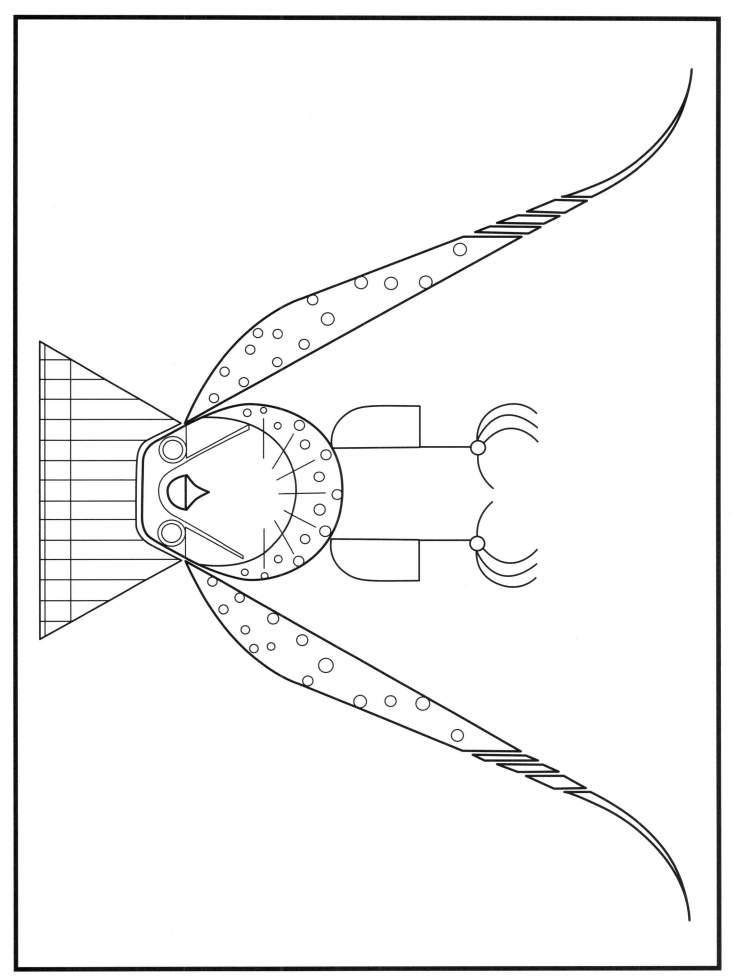

6. The **hawk** perches up high before diving through the air to catch prey in its sharp talons.

7. The tropical **toucan** uses its huge bill to play a game of fruit toss with its mate.

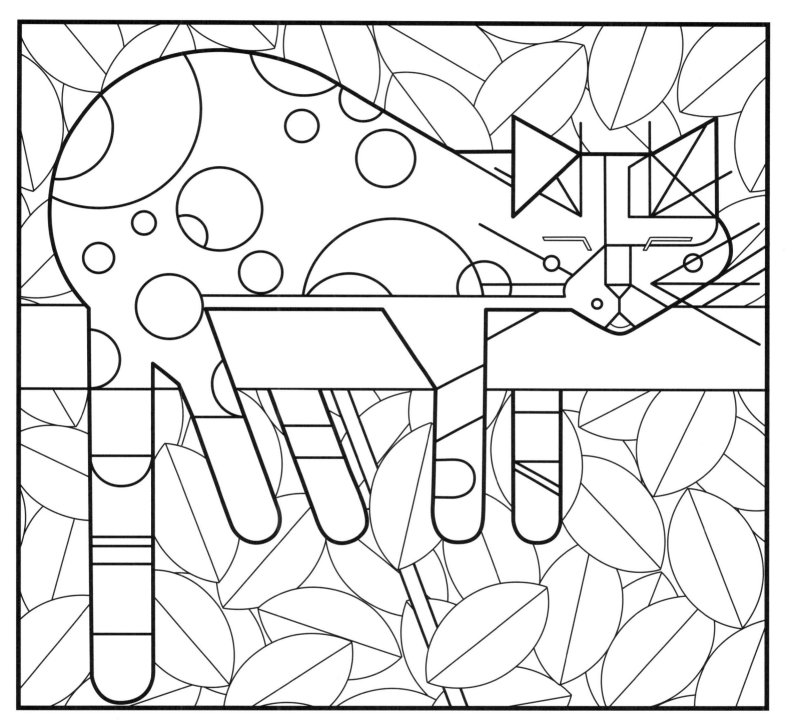

8. A **calico cat**—with white, orange, and black fur—is almost always a female.

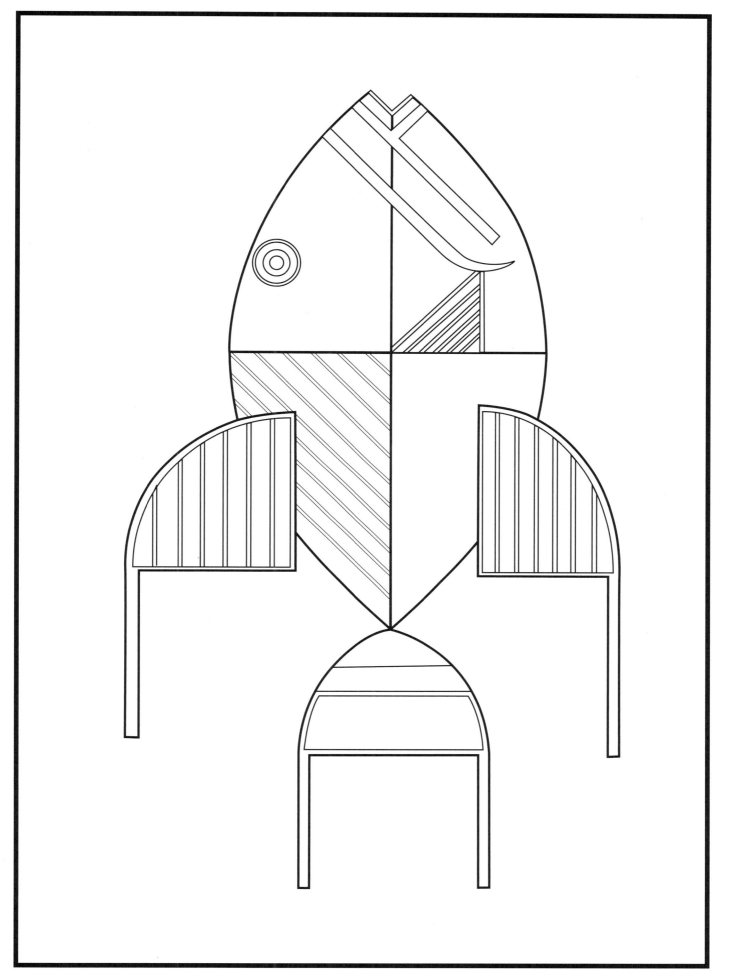

9. Talk about adaptable: the **parrot fish** can change gender and color whenever it wants, and cocoons itself at night to hide from predators.

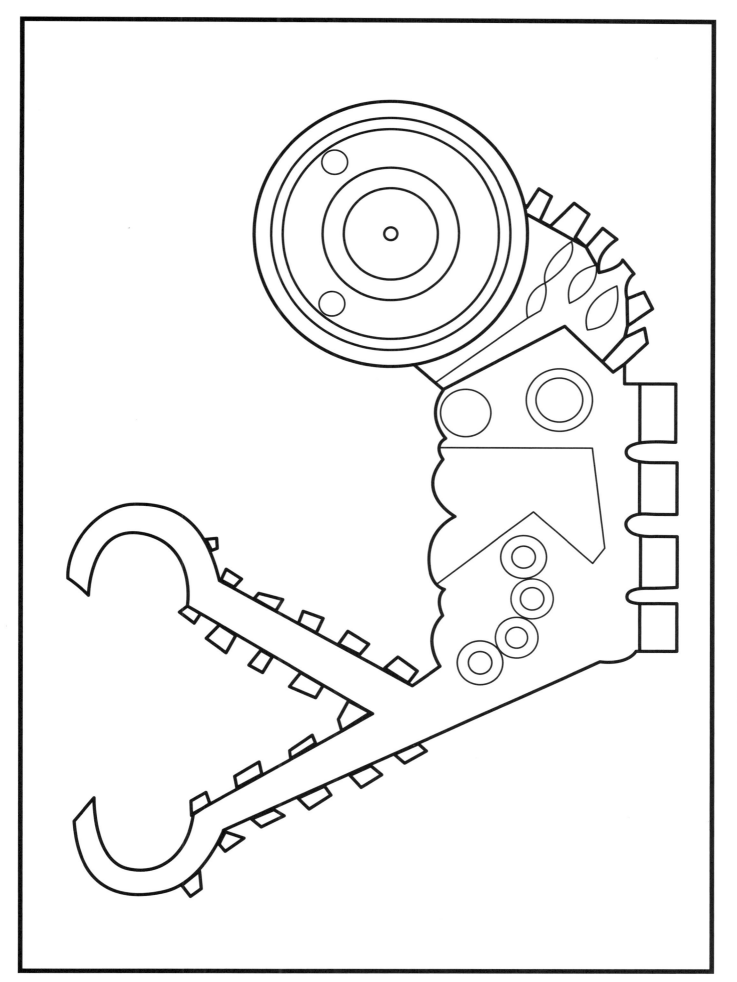

10. The **puss moth caterpillar** stands tall when a predator approaches.

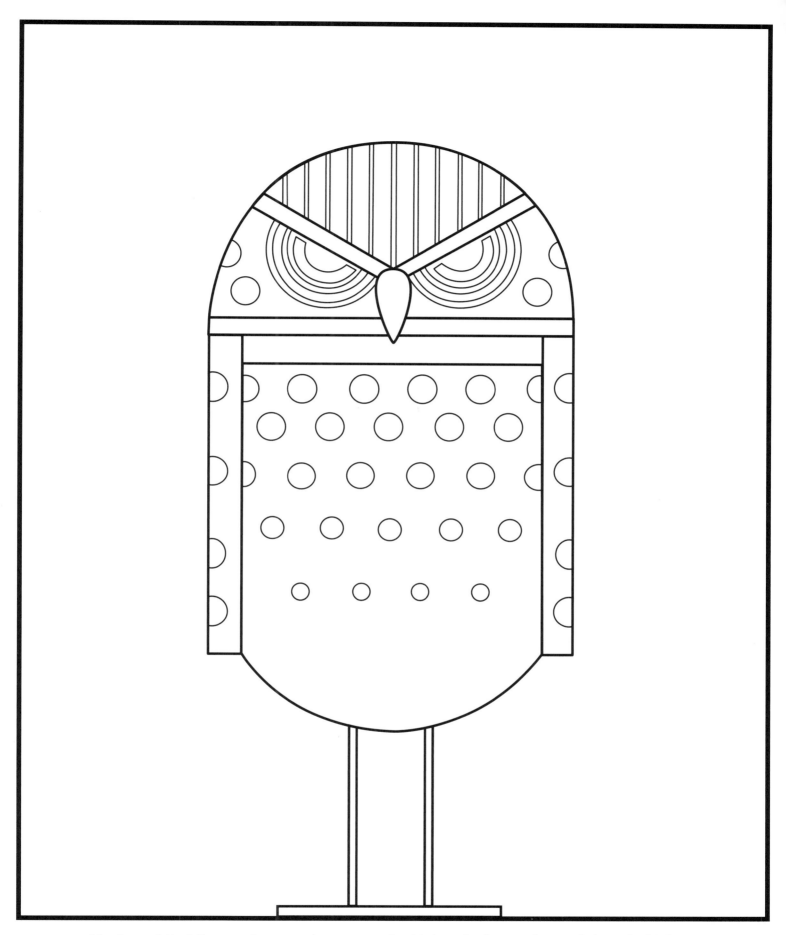

11. An owl that lives underground may sound odd, but the **burrowing owl** doesn't think so.
It nests in holes other animals have left behind.

12. In the Galapagos Islands, the many types of beaks on **Darwin's finches** are so special that they made scientific history.

13. Be mine? The **barn owl** is known for its face shaped like the perfect Valentine's Day heart.

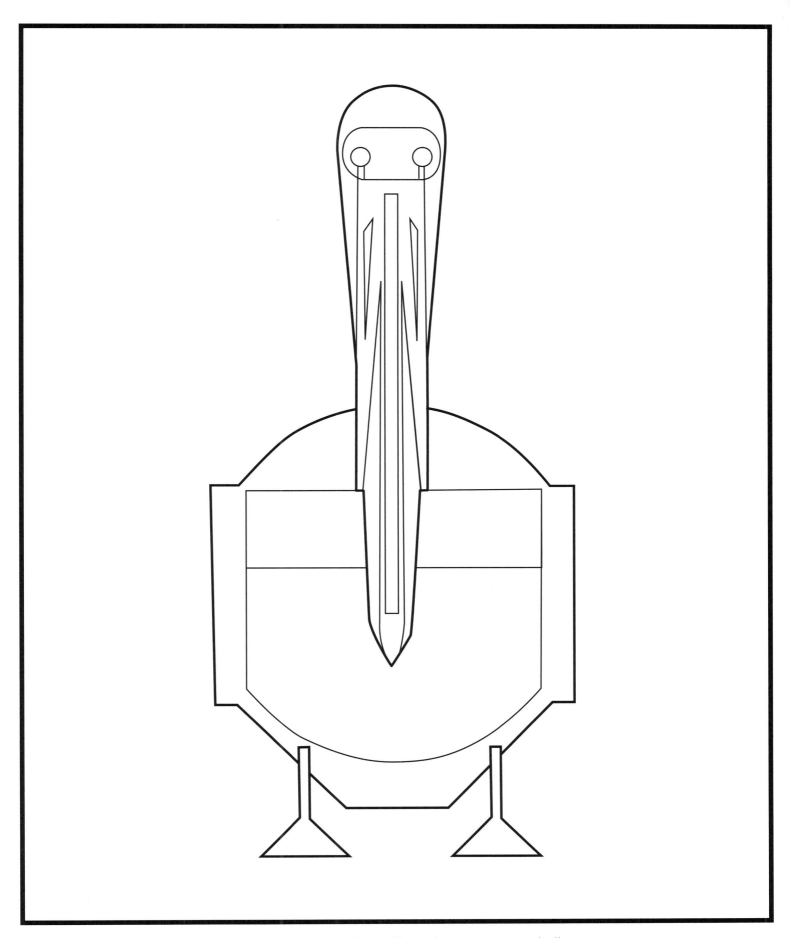

14. Fishing in groups helps the **pelican** drive prey into shallow water,
where it easily scoops up fish in its giant pouch.

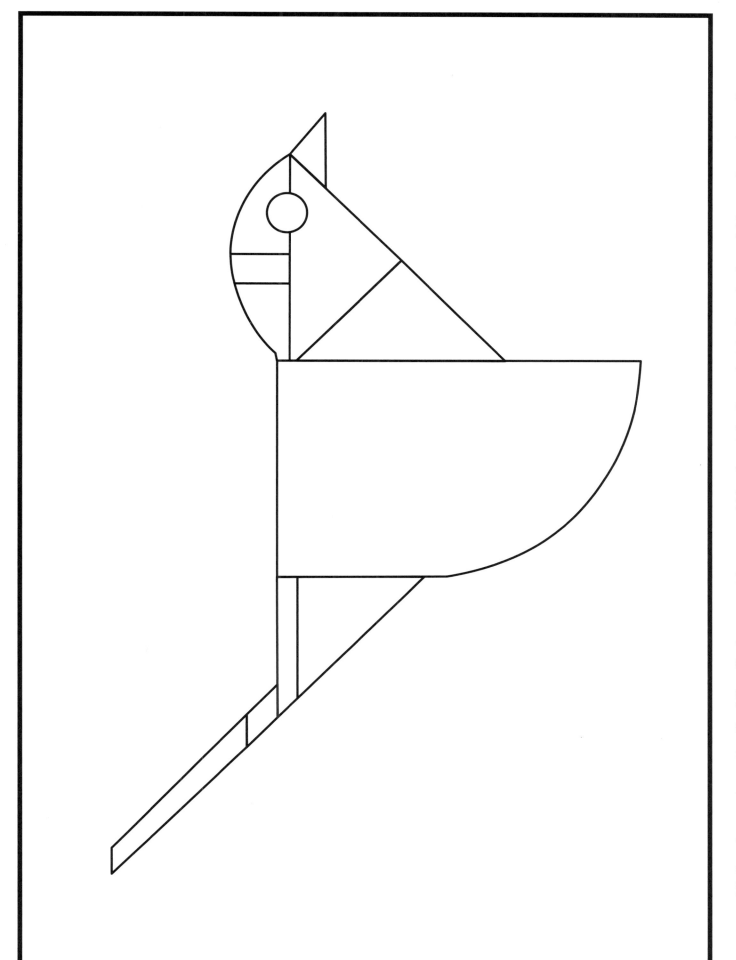

15. People may keep the **Gouldian finch** as a pet because of his vibrant feathers, but he lives in the wild in northern Australia.

16. The male **wood duck** is one of the most spectacular creatures on the lake. His glimmering feathers nearly look painted.

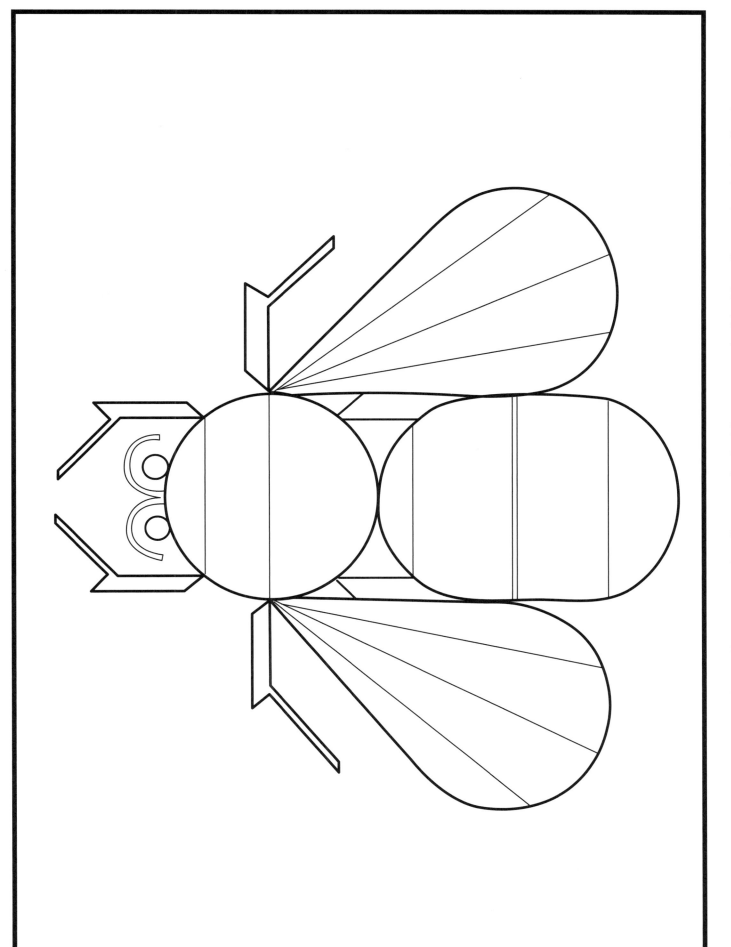

17. A **bumblebee** is so hairy that pollen gets caught all over its body. It's smart, and adds this pollen to the day's collection.

18. You may know the **basset hound** as the lovable dog with the long ears, but this pup was made to use its keen sense of smell for hunting.

19. Pairs of **cardinals** communicate through their sweet song phrases. Singing from her nest, the female may be telling her mate when to bring food home.

20. During autumn migration, the **wood duck** stops in wooded marshes and swamps where there are plenty of acorns and other treats to eat.

21. The **turtle** is one of the oldest types of reptiles, and many are endangered today.

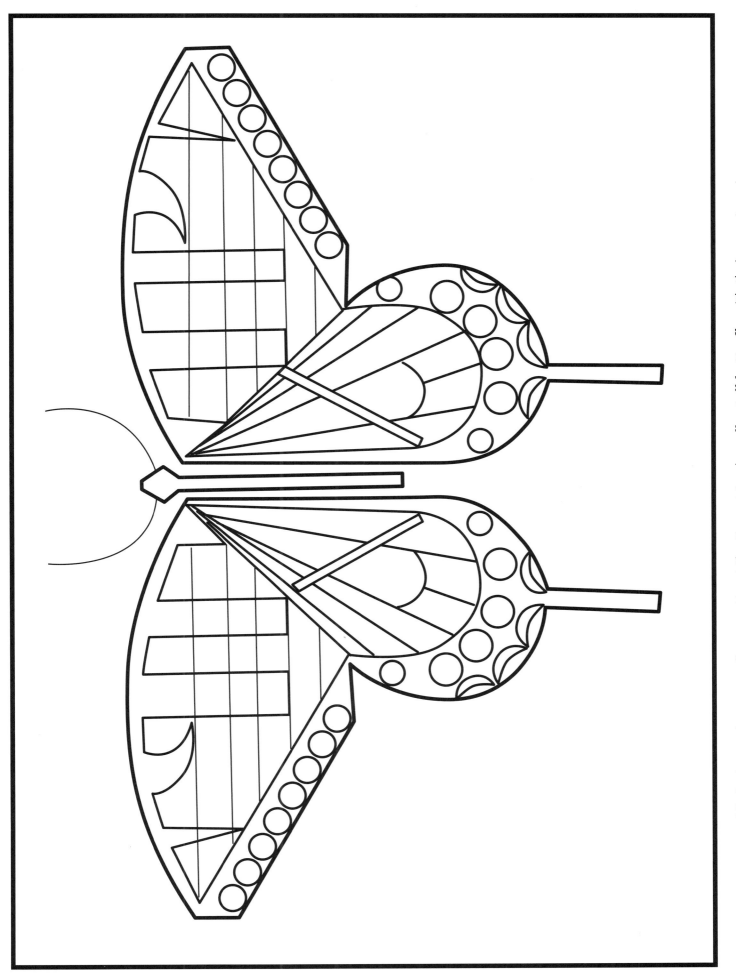

22. Spring and summer flowers attract the tiger-striped **swallowtail butterfly** with their sweet nectar.

Draw and color your own picture here!